INFANT PRAISE

INFANT PRAISE

COMPILED BY

MARGARET KITSON

MUSICAL EDITOR

GUTHRIE FOOTE

LONDON
OXFORD UNIVERSITY PRESS

Oxford University Press, Ely House, London W. 1

GLASGOW NEW YORK TORONTO MELBOURNE WELLINGTON
CAPE TOWN SALISBURY IBADAN NAIROBI DAR ES SALAAM LUSAKA ADDIS ABABA
BOMBAY CALCUTTA MADRAS KARACHI LAHORE DACCA
KUALA LUMPUR SINGAPORE HONG KONG TOKYO

First published 1964
Second impression 1965
Third impression 1967
Fourth impression 1968
Fifth impression 1970

A companion volume, INFANT PRAYER, a practical
treatise on the conduct of the Infant's School assembly, is also published by Oxford University Press,
and contains in Chapter 3, part I a valuable section
on hymn singing in the Infant School

PRINTED IN GREAT BRITAIN

PREFACE

THIS collection of simply worded hymns for very young children was compiled by Margaret Kitson for use with her book *Infant Prayer* (a practical treatise on the conduct of the Infants' School assembly), but it is of equal value when used on its own. The tunes, many of which have not previously appeared elsewhere, match the simplicity of the words, and a fitting complement is provided by the piano accompaniments, which have mostly been arranged by Guthrie Foote.

ACKNOWLEDGEMENTS

GRATEFUL thanks are due to the following who have allowed material for which they own or control the copyright to be included in this book:

WORDS

St. Christopher's College, 74, 80, 90, 91, 92; Miss Margaret Cropper, 48, 70, 73, 81, 89; Mrs. Vera G. Cumberlege, 23, 38; Messrs. J. Curwen & Sons Ltd., 94; Miss Hilda M. Dodd, 86; Messrs. Evans Bros. Ltd., 50, 67; The Fleming H. Revell Co. and Ruth Irwen Rex (from *Sing for Joy*), 47; The Friendship Press and Miss Thomas (from *The Whole World Singing*), 37; Mrs. Lorna Hill, 41; Miss Marion James (Mrs. R. W. Price), 5; Miss Margaret Kitson, 8, 34, 44; The Methodist Youth Department, 79; The National Society, 35, 58, 65, 66, 68, 93; The National Sunday School Union, 18, 45, 55, 57, 60, 85, 87; Oxford University Press (from *Children Praising*), 3, 52: (and the Executors of the Estate of the late F. S. Pierpoint), 4: (and Miss Trump), 26: (from *The Oxford Book of Carols*), 62: (from *Enlarged Songs of Praise*), 99: and 2, 9, 13, 32, 42; The Pilgrim Press, Boston, Mass., U.S.A. (from *Children's Religion*, June 1944), 19; Miss Alice Pullen, 14, 24, 39, 62, 69; The Religious Education Press Ltd., 7, 27, 82, 84; Mrs. Hilda Sanders, 40; The Seabury Press Inc. (from *Sing for Joy*), c 1961: 6, 46, 53, 77, 95; The Rev. A. D. Somerset Ward, 72.

The copyright owners of the following are at present untraceable: 11, 43, 88.

MUSIC

Messrs. J. Curwen & Sons Ltd., 1, 94 i and ii, 99; Mr. Kenneth Finlay, 51; Miss Maud Karpeles, 15 (*mel.*), 55 (*mel.*); The Methodist Youth Department, 49 i; The National Society, 66, 72; Novello & Co. Ltd. (from *The Bird Song*, collected by Cecil J. Sharp), 5 (*mel.*); Oxford University Press (from *Merrily on High*), harm. and/or arr., 59, 62, 63, 64, 68: (from *The English Hymnal*), 2, 11 (*harm.*), 42, 73, 75, 88, 98: (from *Enlarged Songs of Praise*), 91: (and Mr. Guthrie Foote), 20, 21, 25, 74, 81, 83: and 4, 6, 9, 10, 12, 13 (*arr.*), 14, 15 (*harm.*), 18 (*harm.*), 22, 23 (*arr.*), 26, 27, 28 (*arr.*), 30 (*arr.*), 31, 33, 36 (*arr.*), 38, 39, 40 (*arr.*), 44, 45, 46, 48, 50, 52, 54 (*arr.*), 55 (*harm.*), 56 (*arr.*), 57 (*harm.*), 65, 67, 69, 70, 71 (*arr.*), 73, 75, 76 (*arr.*), 78, 79, 82, 84, 85, 86, 87, 93 (*harm.*), 96 (*arr.*), 97 (*arr.*), 100 (*arr.*); Miss Alice Pullen, 24, 62; The Seabury Press Inc. (from *Sing for Joy*), c 1961: 46; Mr. Charles Seeger, 77; Messrs. Stainer & Bell Ltd., 68 (*harm.*). The following are the copyright of The Seabury Press Inc. (from *Sing for Joy*), 1961: the combination of the words and melody of Nos. 47, 53, 77, 95.

Application for the use of any of the following arrangements, which were made especially for this book, must be made to Oxford University Press: 1 i, 1 ii, 2, 3, 5, 6, 8, 9, 10, 11, 12, 14, 15, 17, 18, 19, 21, 22, 24, 25, 27, 29, 31, 34, 35, 37 i, 38, 39, 42, 43, 44, 45, 47, 48, 49 i, 50, 52, 53, 57, 58, 60, 65, 66, 67, 69, 70, 74, 78, 79, 81, 82, 83, 84, 85, 86, 87, 88, 93, 94 i, 95, 98, 99.

CONTENTS

x   CONTENTS

HYMNS

GENERAL

THE WORLD WHICH OUR FATHER MADE

1 ROYAL OAK 7676 and refrain.

Adapted by MARTIN SHAW, 1875–1958, from an English Traditional Melody

ALTERNATIVE TUNE

ALL THINGS BRIGHT AND BEAUTIFUL 7676 and refrain. WILLIAM HENRY MONK
1823–89

THE WORLD WHICH OUR FATHER MADE

*A*LL *things bright and beautiful,*
  All creatures great and small,
All things wise and wonderful,
The Lord God made them all.

2 Each little flower that opens,
  Each little bird that sings;
  He made their glowing colours,
  He made their tiny wings.

3 The cold wind in the winter,
  The pleasant summer sun,
  The ripe fruits in the garden,
  He made them every one.

4. He gave us eyes to see them,
  And lips that we might tell
  How great is God Almighty,
  Who has made all things well.

        Mrs. Cecil Frances Alexander (1818–95)

3

2 KING'S LANGLEY C.M.   English Traditional May-day Carol

ALL things which live below the sky
Or move within the sea,
Are creatures of the Lord most high
And brothers unto me.

2 I love to hear the robin sing,
Perched on the highest bough;
To see the rook with purple wing
Follow the shining plough;

3 The seagull whiter than the foam,
The fish that dart beneath,
The lowing cattle coming home,
The goats upon the heath.

4. Almighty Father, King of kings
And lover of the meek,
Make me a friend of helpless things,
Defender of the weak.

Edward John Brailsford (1841–1921)

4

3 ST. FLAVIAN C.M.   Adapted from Psalm 132 in *Day's Psalter*, 1563

DOWN deep dark mines below the ground,
  Fathers and brothers toil,
And dig for coal to warm our homes,
And make our kettles boil.

2. Thank God for coal! God bless the men
  Who work in cheerless gloom,
  And when their daily toil is done,
  God bring them safely home.

William Main Page (1869–1940)

4 ENGLAND'S LANE 7777·77

Adapted from an English Melody, by
GEOFFREY SHAW, 1879–1943

FOR the beauty of the earth,
  For the beauty of the skies,
For the love which from our birth
Over and around us lies,
Lord of all, to thee we raise
This our grateful hymn of praise.

2. For the beauty of each hour
Of the day and of the night,
Hill and vale, and tree and flower,
Sun and moon and stars of light,
Lord of all, to thee we raise
This our grateful hymn of praise.

Folliott Sandford Pierpoint (1835–1917)

5 BIRD SONG L.M.

English Traditional Melody collected
by CECIL SHARP, 1859–1924

GOD of the rabbits, keep them warm,
Safe in the cold and heavy storm.
God of the sparrows, be their guide,
Show them a little place to hide.

2. God of the squirrels, help them store
Acorns I dropped outside my door.
God of the small things, keep them fed,
Give to each one, a warm, dry bed.

Marion James

6 MY PLACE 76   HUBERT GRIERSON

G OD who put the stars in space,
Who made the world we share,
In his making made a place
For me, and put me here.

2. Thank you, God, for stars in space
And for the world we share.
Thank you for my special place
To love and serve you here.

Norman and Margaret Mealy
based on a poem by Lucile S. Reid

THE WORLD WHICH OUR FATHER MADE

7 THINGS I LOVE 4444

GWEN F. SMITH

I LOVE the sun[1]
It shines on me,
God made the sun,
And God made me.

2 I love the stars,
They twinkle on me,
God made the stars,
And God made me.

3 I love the flowers,
They smile at me,
God made the flowers,
And God made me.

4 I love the rain[2]
It splashes on me,
God made the rain,
And God made me.

5 I love the wind,
It blows round me,
God made the wind,
And God made me.

6. I love the birds,
They sing to me,
God made the birds,
And God made me.

Gwen F. Smith

[1] *Or* moon.
[2] *Or* sea.

9

8 CARLISLE S.M.   CHARLES LOCKHART, 1745-1815

I OFTEN think of God:
  He made the world I see;
And if he made such lovely things
How lovely God must be.

2. I often think of God:
   I know that he made me;
   And if I am his loving child
   How happy I shall be.

Margaret Kitson

THE WORLD WHICH OUR FATHER MADE

9 REFLECTIONS 11 11. 11 11   PAUL STRINGER

O FATHER, the maker of beautiful things,
   Like roses and daisies and butterflies' wings,
And mountains and forests, and water and snow:
All show us thy love for thou makest them so.

2 All creatures are thine in the world and beyond,
   The bee in the pollen, the fish in the pond,
   The fox in his burrow, the bird on the bough:
   All show us thy love for thou makest them so.

3. The lambs and the calves and the foals that are born,
   The beans and potatoes, the roots and the corn,
   The apple and cherry trees, row after row:
   All show us thy love for thou makest them so.

                                    Percy Dearmer (1867–1936)

10 OVER THE EARTH 9696.8696

Scottish Tune

OVER the earth is a mat of green,
Over the green is dew,
Over the dew are the arching trees,
Over the trees the blue.
Across the blue are scudding clouds,
Over the clouds the sun
Over it all is the love of God
Blessing us ev'ry one.

Author unknown

THE WORLD WHICH OUR FATHER MADE

11 PLEADING SAVIOUR 11 9 11 9.11 9   *Plymouth Collection* (U.S.A.), 1885

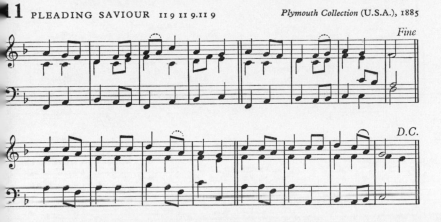

OVER the sea there are little brown children,
  Fathers and mothers and babies dear;
They have not heard of the Father in heaven,
No one has told them that God is near.
Swift let the message go over the water,
Telling the children God is near.

2. Sometimes at night when the darkness gathers,
  Little brown children begin to fear;
  They have not heard of the dear Lord Jesus,
  No one has told them that he is near.

Hetty Lee Holland

12 PAPOOSE Irregular   JOAN WHITE

THE clever papoose in the wigwam that lives,
Whose life is so happy and free,
Is my Indian brother;
And Jesus loves him
Just as he loves you and me.

2 The Eskimo babies are wrapped all in fur;
They live in the north country,
Where cold winds blow;
And Jesus loves them
Just as he loves you and me.

3 The little Jap babies, with shining dark eyes,
Live on a green isle in the sea,
Too many to count;
And Jesus loves them
Just as he loves you and me.

4. The pretty brown babies, who roll in the sand,
In a country far over the sea,
Are my African brothers;
And Jesus loves them
Just as he loves you and me.

Margaret Coote Brown

14

13 MORNING HYMN L.M.   FRANÇOIS HIPPOLITE BARTHÉLÉMON, 1741–1808

TO God who makes all lovely things
How happy must our praises be!
Each day a new surprise he brings
To make us glad his world to see.

2 How plentiful must be the mines
From which he gives his gold away;
In March he gives us celandines,
He gives us buttercups in May.

3 On winter nights his quiet flakes
Come falling, falling all the night,
And when the world next morning wakes
It finds itself in robes of white!

4 He made the sea that shines afar
With waves that dance unceasingly,
And every single tiny star
That sparkles in the evening sky.

5. He made the people that I meet,
The many people, great and small,
In home and school, and down the street,
And he made me to love them all.

John MacLeod Campbell Crum (1872–1958)

14 PRAISING THEE S.M.

JOHN STARR

WE praise thee for the sun,
  The golden shining sun,
That gives us healing, strength and joy,
We praise thee for the sun.

2 We praise thee for the rain,
  The softly falling rain,
That gives us healing, strength and joy,
We praise thee for the rain.

3. We praise thee for thy love,
  Our friend and Father God,
Who gives us healing, strength and joy,
We praise thee for thy love.

Alice Muriel Pullen

THE WORLD WHICH OUR FATHER MADE

15 BUTLER C.M.

English Traditional Melody

WHEN lamps are lighted in the town,
  The boats sail out to sea,
The fishers watch when night comes down,
They work for you and me.

2. We little children go to rest—
  Before we sleep we'll pray
That God will bless the fishermen
And guard them night and day.

  Maria Matilda Penstone (1859–1910), *altered*

GOD'S PRESENCE, HIS BLESSING AND HIS CARE

16   *To be sung to* CRADLE SONG, *No.* 59

BE near me, Lord Jesus; I ask thee to stay
Close by me for ever, and love me, I pray.
Bless all the dear children in thy tender care,
And fit us for heaven, to live with thee there.

Anonymous

17 ORIENTIS PARTIBUS 77.77   Old French Melody

FATHER, lead me day by day
Ever in thy own sweet way;
Teach me to be pure and true,
Show me what I ought to do.

2. May I do the good I know,
Be thy loving child below,
Then at last go home to thee,
Evermore thy child to be.

John Page Hopps (1834–1912)

18 BUCKLAND 77.77

LEIGHTON GEORGE HAYNE, 1836–83

FATHER, see thy children here,
For thy blessing drawing near;
Listen to us as we pray,
Help us in our school today.

E. G Wallis

19 STUTTGART 8787

Adapted from a Melody in *Psalmodi*
Sacra, Gotha, 171

GLADLY lift we hearts and voices
Unto thee, O God, in prayer;
Knowing thou art always with us,
Thou art with us everywhere.

2 Everyone is sometimes frightened,
Sometimes has hard things to do.
Help us know that thou art with us,
Thou canst keep us strong and true.

3. Gladly lift we hearts and voices
Unto thee, O God, in prayer;
Knowing thou art always with us,
Thou art with us everywhere.

Florence M. Taylor

20 TWINEHAM Irregular

English Traditional Melody (Sussex)
collected by GUTHRIE FOOTE

GOD has given us a book full of stories,
Which was made for his people of old,
It begins with the tale of a garden,
And ends with the city of gold.

2. There are stories for parents and children,
For the old who are ready to rest,
But for all who can read them or listen,
The story of Jesus is best.

Maria Matilda Penstone (1859–1910)

21 PETITION 666.5   GUTHRIE FOOT

small notes piano

A - men

GOD, the Father, bless us;
God, the Son, defend us;
God, the Spirit, keep us,
Now and evermore. *Amen.*

Author Unknown

22 MY FATHER'S CARE 888.4   HUBERT GRIERSON

H OW strong and sweet my Father's care,
   That round about me like the air
Is with me always ev'rywhere.
He cares for me.

2. Dear God and Father, let me know
   Thy love will guide me where I go;
   And let my heart for ever glow
   With love to thee.

Verse 1. Anonymous
Verse 2. William H. Hamilton (1886–1958)

23 DUNDEE C.M.

Scottish Psalter, 1615, as given in
Ravenscroft's Psalter (rhythm adapted

I LOVE the Lord who is my strength,
My Saviour, God and Might.
His strong hand stretches out to me
In day or darkest night.

2 I trust the Lord when thunder rolls
Or darkness frightens me.
When I am hurt or sad or ill
Close to my side he'll be.

3. I pray the Lord to make me brave
In all I do or say.
He has the strength to make me strong
To drive my fears away.

Vera G. Cumberlege

24 I'M VERY GLAD OF GOD 6684   ALICE MURIEL PULLEN

I'M very glad of God:
His love takes care of me,
In every lovely thing I see
God smiles at me!

2. I'm very glad of God:
His love takes care of me
In every lovely sound I hear
God speaks to me!

Alice Muriel Pullen

25 INTO THY KEEPING 6564

GUTHRIE FOOTE

small notes piano

A - men

INTO thy loving care,
Into thy keeping,
Lord, who art ev'rywhere,
Take us, we pray. *Amen.*

Anonymous

26 WESTRIDGE 8583   MARTIN SHAW, 1875–1958

JESUS, friend of little children,
    Be a friend to me;
Take my hand and ever keep me
Close to thee.

Walter John Mathams (1853–1931)

27 TRUST 8585

PAUL STRINGER

LOVING Father of all children,
I belong to thee;
Through the day-time, through the night-time.
Please take care of me.

Author Unknown

28 INNOCENTS 77.77   Composed or adapted by JOSEPH SMITH, 1800–73

LOVING Shepherd of thy sheep,
Keep thy lamb, in safety keep;
Nothing can thy power withstand,
None can pluck me from thy hand.

2 Loving Shepherd, ever near,
Teach thy lamb thy voice to hear;
Suffer not my steps to stray
From the straight and narrow way.

3. Where thou leadest I would go,
Walking in thy steps below,
Till before my Father's throne
I shall know as I am known.
                    Jane Eliza Leeson (1809–81)

29 DOMINUS REGIT ME 8787   JOHN BACCHUS DYKES, 1823–76

T HE King of love my Shepherd is,
  Whose goodness faileth never;
I nothing lack if I am his
And he is mine for ever.

2. And so through all the length of days
Thy goodness faileth never:
Good Shepherd, may I sing thy praise
Within thy house for ever.

Sir Henry Williams Baker (1821–77)

PRAISE AND THANKSGIVING

30   *To be sung to* WIR PFLÜGEN *(refrain only), No.* 56

ALL good gifts around us
Are sent from heaven above,
Then thank the Lord, O thank the Lord,
For all his love.

Matthias Claudius (1740–1815)
Tr. Jane Montgomery Campbell (1817–78)

31 WELL-BEING S.M.   JOHN STARR

FOR all the strength we have,
To run and leap and play,
For all our limbs so sound and strong,
We thank thee, Lord, today.

2. Make all thy children, Lord,
Healthy and strong like me,
To run and leap and shout and play,
And praise thee in our glee.

Maria Matilda Penstone (1859–1910)

32

To be sung to STUTTGART, *No.* 19

HOLY God, to thee our voices
We, thy thankful children raise,
Father, Son, and Holy Spirit,
Listen to our hymn of praise.

Margaret Owen

33 HOLY, HOLY, HOLY 6573   HERBERT WISEMAN

HOLY, Holy, Holy,
Holy is the Lord—
Heav'n and Earth are praising thee,
Lord most high.

PRAISE AND THANKSGIVING

34 HEATHLANDS 77.77.77   HENRY SMART, 1813–79

I CAN praise God all day long,
I can sing him my own song,
Praise him in my work and play,
Praise him, praise him all the day,
I can praise God all day long,
I can sing him my own song.

Margaret Kitson

33   D

35 DAILY, DAILY 8787.D   Old French Melody

L ET us thank the Heavenly Father
 For the friends we love today,
For the houses that we live in,
And the places where we play;
Father, mother, brother, sister,
And all creatures great and small;
For God made them, and he made us
To be friendly to them all.

Hetty Lee Holland, altered

36 NUN DANKET 6767.6666 JOHANN CRÜGER, 1598–1662

NOW thank we all our God,
    With heart and hands and voices,
Who wondrous things hath done,
In whom his world rejoices;
Who from our mother's arms
Hath blessed us on our way
With countless gifts of love,
And still is ours today.

Martin Rinkart (1586–1649)
Tr. Catherine Winkworth (1827–78)

35

37 PRAISE AND THANKSGIVING 10. 10. 8   Alsatian Melody

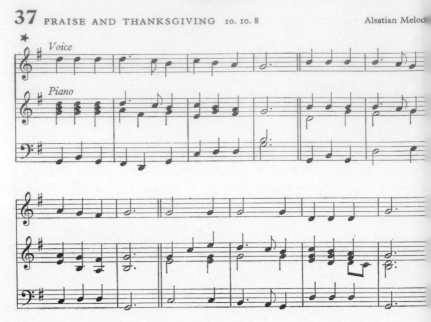

* *This version must not be used if the tune is sung as a round.*

PRAISE and thanksgiving let everyone bring
Unto our Father for every good thing!
All together joyfully sing!

Edith Lovell Thomas
from the German 'Lobet und preiset'

PRAISE AND THANKSGIVING
ALTERNATIVE VERSION
(as a round)

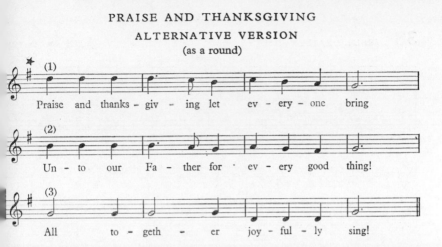

Praise and thanks – giv – ing let ev – ery – one bring

Un – to our Fa – ther for ᐧ ev – ery good thing!

All to – geth – er joy – ful – ly sing!

* *One singer begins alone and when he reaches* (2) *the second singer starts to sing from* (1). *When the first singer reaches* (3) *a third singer may begin at* (1).

38 JOYFUL PRAISES C.M.

GEORGE HAYWAR

SING a glad song to Christ the King,
He wants us to be gay.
Praise him with clear and happy voice,
Bring joy to each new day.

2 Dance a glad dance to praise his name,
Jump high and skip and run.
Thank him for health and dancing feet,
For laughter, play and fun.

3. Play him a tune on drums and pipe,
Bang cymbals loud and long.
Serve him with gladness and with love,
Come near him with a song.

Vera G. Cumberlege

39 GLAD VOICES 8485.8485   WARWICK FARRINGDON

SING praises, sing praises to God,
Joyfully sing.
Sing praises, sing praises to God,
Let glad voices ring.
Sing praises, sing praises to God,
Joyfully sing.
Sing praises, sing praises to God,
For each lovely thing.

Alice Muriel Pullen

40 BATTISHILL 77.77

Adapted from a Melody by JONATHAN
BATTISHILL, 1738–1801

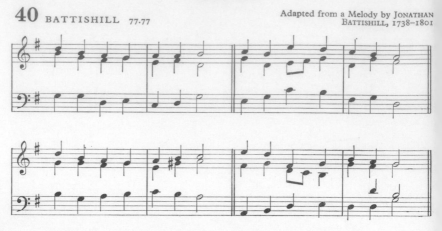

THANK you for my mother dear,
Always loving, always near:
Help me show in all I do,
That I really love her too.

Hilda Sanders

41

To be sung to BATTISHILL, *No.* 40

THANK you! for the world so sweet,
Thank you! for the food we eat,
Thank you! for the birds that sing,
Thank you! God, for everything.

Edith Rutter Leatham (1870–1939)

42 SUSSEX 8787

English Traditional Melody
(adapted)

THANK you, God, for all you give us,
Parents, home, and friends so dear,
For the blossom in our gardens,
For the birds' song, sweet and clear.

Margaret Owen

43 ST. STEPHEN C.M.   WILLIAM JONES, 1726–1800

WE have so much to thank you for,
   Our heav'nly Father dear:
For life and love and tender care,
Through all the happy year;

2. For homes and friends and daily food,
   Each one a gift of love.
For ev'ry good and perfect gift
Is from our God above.

Ira F. Seydon

WORKING FOR GOD

44 WORKING FOR GOD 75.75.7775   HUBERT GRIERSON

G OD has given us work to do,
  Work to do for him.
God has given us friends to help,
Friends to help for him.
We will work for God today,
We will help our friends today,
We shall be so glad today,
Glad to work for him.

Margaret Kitson

43

45 GIFTS 7779

JAMES HEATH

HANDS to work and feet to run—
God's good gifts to me and you;
Hands and feet he gave to us
To help each other the whole day through.

2 Eyes to see and ears to hear—
God's good gifts to me and you;
Eyes and ears he gave to us
To help each other the whole day through.

3. Minds to think and hearts to love—
God's good gifts to me and you;
Minds and hearts he gave to us
To help each other the whole day through.

Hilda Margaret Dodd

WORKING FOR GOD

46 HELP OUR LIPS 666

JOHN HARRELL

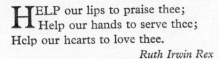

H ELP our lips to praise thee;
   Help our hands to serve thee;
Help our hearts to love thee.

Ruth Irwin Rex

47 WILLING HANDS L.M.

JULIAN CHANT

H ERE are my hands to work for thee,
Take them and make them work for thee.
Here are my feet to walk thy way,
Take them and make them walk thy way.

2. Here are my eyes to see the right,
Take them and make them see the right.
Here is my life to give to thee,
Take me and make me more like thee.

Ruth B. Pierce

WORKING FOR GOD

48 EAST HORNDON Irregular

English Traditional Melody

I HAVE a clear message from Jesus, my King,
Which I'm trying to keep in my mind,
He said 'Love one another' so I must find out
The way to be loving and kind.

2. Perhaps I can make people happy at home,
And if I remember I'll find
The people that Jesus would want me to help;
I must try to be loving and kind.

Margaret Cropper

49 NIGHTINGALE 10 11.10 10   H. J. STAPLES, 1891–194[ ]

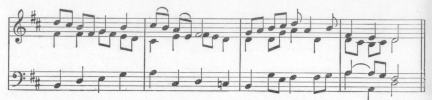

ALTERNATIVE TUNE

JESUS BIDS US SHINE 10 11.10 10   EDWIN OTHELLO EXCELL, 1852–1921

JESUS bids us shine with a pure clear light,
Like a little candle burning in the night;
In this world of darkness, we must shine—
You in your small corner, and I in mine.

WORKING FOR GOD

2 Jesus bids us shine, first of all for him;
Well he sees and knows it, if our light is dim;
He looks from heaven, to see us shine—
You in your small corner, and I in mine.

3. Jesus bids us shine then for all around;
Many kinds of darkness in this world abound:
Sin and want and sorrow; so we must shine—
You in your small corner, and I in mine.

Susan Warner (1819–85)

50 HEAR OUR PRAYER 5575   VICTOR SOUTHERN

JESUS, hear our prayer,
We thy friends would be:
Help us to be true and brave
As we think of thee.

Mary Osborn

GIVING AND ASKING FORGIVENESS

51 GLENFINLAS 6565   KENNETH GEORGE FINL.

HERE we come with gladness,
Gifts of love to bring,
Praising him who loves us—
Christ the Saviour King.

2. More and more for Jesus
May we gladly give;
Giving, giving, giving,
Is the way to live.
Julia Harriette Johnston (1849–1919)

2 OFFERINGS 8684

JOHN STARR

WE pray thee, Father, to accept
The loving gifts we make;
O, wilt thou take them with our love,
For Jesus' sake?

Phoebe Armitage

3 SONG 13 7777

Based on Song 13 by ORLANDO GIBBONS,
1583–1625

FOR the things that I've done wrong,
Things that I remember long,
Hurting friends and those I love,
I am very sorry God.

John Harrell

AUTUMN TERM

HARVEST

54 ST. GEORGE 77.77.D

Sir George Elvey, 1816

COME, ye thankful people, come,
Raise the song of harvest-home!
All be safely gathered in,
Ere the winter storms begin;
God, our maker, doth provide
For our wants to be supplied;
Come to God's own temple, come;
Raise the song of harvest-home!

Henry Alford (1810–71)

HARVEST

5 JOYS SEVEN 7575 and Refrain   English Traditional Carol

    S EE the farmer sow the seed
      While the field is brown;
See the furrows deep and straight
Up the field and down.
Farmer, farmer, sow your seed
Up the field and down;
God will make the golden corn
Grow where all is brown.

2. Wait awhile and look again
    Where the field was bare;
    See how God has sent the corn
    Growing golden there.

        Frederick Arthur Jackson (1867–1942)

56 WIR PFLÜGEN 7676.D. and Refrain

JOHANN SCHULZ, 1747–18

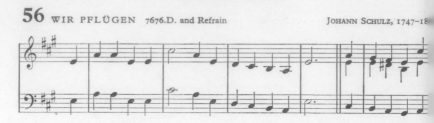

Refrain

HARVEST

WE plough the fields, and scatter
   The good seed on the land,
But it is fed and watered
By God's almighty hand;
He sends the snow in winter,
The warmth to swell the grain,
The breezes and the sunshine,
And soft refreshing rain:
All good gifts around us
Are sent from heaven above,
Then thank the Lord, O thank the Lord,
For all his love.

       Matthias Claudius (1740–1815)
       Tr. Jane Montgomery Campbell (1817–78)

57 NORTH COATES 6565 TIMOTHY RICHARD MATTHEWS, 1826-191

WHEN the corn is planted
In the deep dark bed,
Mothers know their children
Will have daily bread.

2 God sends sun and showers,
Birds sing overhead,
While the corn is growing
For our daily bread.

3. When the corn is gathered,
Stored in barn and shed,
Then we all are thankful
For our daily bread.

Anonymous

ADVENT

58 WELSH CAROL 10 11.11 11   Traditional Welsh Tune

CHRISTMAS is coming, is coming again
And bringing its message of goodwill to men.
The holly and ivy, the mistletoe now
Are gay with the berries that hang from the bough.

2. Jesus is coming, is coming again
And bringing his message of goodwill to men.
The Babe who is sleeping in Bethlehem's stall
Is Son of the Father, and Brother of all.

Phyllis Saunders

CHRISTMAS

59 CRADLE SONG 11 11.11 11   WILLIAM JAMES KIRKPATRICK, 1838–1921

A WAY in a manger, no crib for a bed,
    The little Lord Jesus laid down his sweet head.
The stars in the bright sky looked down where he lay
The little Lord Jesus asleep on the hay.

Anonymous

60 BABY JESUS, SLEEPING SOFTLY 8787   HILDA MARGARET DODD

B ABY Jesus, sleeping softly
  On the warm and fragrant hay,
Children all the wide world over
Think of you on Christmas Day.

2 Mother Mary watching Jesus
Sleeping in the soft warm hay,
Children all the wide world over
Think of you on Christmas Day.

3. Joseph standing close beside them
Hearing what the shepherds say,
Children all the wide world over
Think of you on Christmas Day.

Hilda Margaret Dodd

61 JESUS, BABY JESUS 664 ALICE MURIEL PULLEN

J ESUS, Baby Jesus,
  Mother Mary loves you,
Rocks you to sleep.

2 Jesus, Baby Jesus,
    Shepherds run to find you,
    Leaving their sheep.

3 Jesus, Baby Jesus,
    Wise Men come to find you:
    A star leads the way.

4. Jesus, Baby Jesus,
    All the children love you,
    Love Christmas Day.
              Alice Muriel Pullen

62 ROCKING 10 7.88.77

Melody 'Hajej Nynjej' (Czechoslovakian

LITTLE Jesus, sweetly sleep, do not stir,
We will lend a coat of fur,
We will rock you, rock you, rock you,
We will rock you, rock you, rock you:
See the fur to keep you warm,
Snugly round your tiny form.

2. Mary's little baby, sleep, sweetly sleep,
Sleep in comfort, slumber deep;
We will rock you, rock you, rock you,
We will rock you, rock you, rock you:
We will serve you all we can,
Darling, darling little man.

Czech Carol
Tr. Percy Dearmer (1867–1936)

63 ADESTE FIDELES Irregular   JOHN FRANCIS WADE, *c.* 1711–86

O COME, all ye faithful,
    Joyful and triumphant,
O come ye, O come ye to Bethlehem;
Come and behold him,
Born the King of Angels:
O come, let us adore him,
O come, let us adore him,
O come, let us adore him, Christ the Lord.

John Francis Wade (*c.* 1711–86)

64 IRBY 8787.77

HENRY JOHN GAUNTLETT, 1805–76

ONCE in royal David's city
  Stood a lowly cattle shed,
Where a mother laid her baby
In a manger for his bed:
Mary was that mother mild,
Jesus Christ her little child.

Mrs. Cecil Frances Alexander (1818–95)

65 CHRISTMAS CANDLES 6565.D

JOAN WHITE

SING a song of candles
Round the Christmas tree;
Sing a song of candles
Round the Christmas tree;
Look, they shine for Jesus
On his mother's knee.
Look, they shine for Jesus
On his mother's knee.

G. Starr

EASTER TERM

EPIPHANY

66 OVER THE HILLS 8886

PHYLLIS SAUNDERS

1. OVER the hills to Bethlehem
Who comes this way? Who
comes this way?
Over the hills to Bethlehem
Who comes this way today?

2. Here come three Kings to Bethle-
hem,
Riding this way. Riding this way.
Here come three Kings to Bethle-
hem
Riding this way today.

3. I am a King from lands afar,
Rich gold I bring, gift for the
King.
I am a King from lands afar
Following yonder star.

4. I am a King from lands afar
Incense I bring, gift for the King.
I am a King from lands afar
Following yonder star.

5. I am a King from lands afar
And Myrrh I bring, gift for the King.
I am a King from lands afar
Following yonder star.

6. Over the hills from Bethlehem
Who rides away? Who rides away?
Over the hills from Bethlehem
Who rides another way?

7. Three Kings have gone from Bethlehem
Riding away. Riding away.
Three Kings have gone from Bethlehem
Home by another way.

Phyllis Saunders

THE CHILDHOOD OF JESUS

67 CHILD OF MARY 6565   ELIZABETH HARE

JESUS, child of Mary,
  Hear us as we pray.
Be our unseen playmate
This and every day.

2 And when play is over,
    Bless the work we do,
    Jesus, in our school-time,
    Be our comrade, too.

3. Help us, child of Mary,
    In our work and play;
    Teach us to be like thee
    This and every day.

Mary Osborn

68 SUSSEX CAROL 88.88.88   English Traditional Carol

THE Holy Child went to and fro,
In Mary's home of long ago,
And when his mother called his name,
How quickly he rose up and came!
Lord Jesus, in my home today
I pray thee help me to obey.

2. The Holy Child went to and fro
In Nazareth so long ago;
The boys who shared his playtime there
Would always find him kind and fair.
Lord Jesus, bless me in my play
And keep me kind and fair today.

G. Starr

THE MINISTRY OF JESUS

69 IN GALILEE 8585

GEORGE HAYWARD

I N Galilee beside the sea
Little girls and boys
Came to Jesus, talked with Jesus;
Jesus shared their joys.

2. In Galilee beside the sea
People who were sad
Came to Jesus, sent for Jesus;
Jesus made them glad.

Alice Muriel Pullen

70 KINDLINESS 11.11.11.11   JULIAN CHANT

JESUS' hands were kind hands, doing good to all;
  Healing pain and sickness, blessing children small;
Washing tired feet, and saving those who fall;
Jesus' hands were kind hands, doing good to all.

2. Take my hands, Lord Jesus, let them work for you,
   Make them strong and gentle, kind in all I do;
   Let me watch you, Jesus, till I'm gentle too,
   Till my hands are kind hands, quick to work for you.

                                        Margaret Cropper

PALM SUNDAY

71 ST. THEODULPH 7676.D   MELCHIOR TESCHNER, c. 1615

Fine

D.C.

ALL glory, laud, and honour
To thee, Redeemer, King,
To whom the lips of children
Made sweet hosannas ring.

2 Thou didst accept their praises
Accept the prayers we bring,
Who in all good delightest,
Thou good and gracious King.

3. All glory, laud, and honour
To thee, Redeemer, King,
To whom the lips of children
Made sweet hosannas ring.

St. Theodulph of Orleans (c. 750–821)
Tr. John Mason Neale (1818–66)

72 DUNKIRK VARIATION 9696   A. R. B. WYLAM

RIDING, riding, who is this riding
   Clothed in a robe of white?
Children, children, why do the children
Run out to see the sight?

2. Riding, riding, Jesus is riding
   Into Jerusalem.
   Children, children, all little children
   Know that he loveth them.

Reginald Somerset Ward

73 CAPEL C.M.

English Traditional Melody

THE glory of our King was seen
When he came riding by,
And all the children waved and sang
Hosaanna, King most high!

2. The glory of our King was seen
When, with his arms stretched wide,
To show his love to everyone
Jesus was crucified.

Margaret Cropper

74 HARVEST SONG 8787.D   GUTHRIE FOOTE

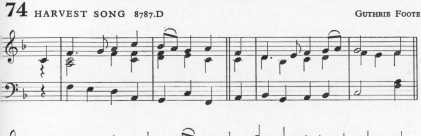

TO Jesus Christ the children sang
Hosanna, Lord! Hosanna!
Through city streets their voices rang,
Hosanna, Lord! Hosanna!
To Jesus Christ, the children's King,
Hosanna, Lord! Hosanna!
With joyful hearts our praise we bring;
Hosanna, Lord! Hosanna!

Alda M. Milner-Barry

73

GOOD FRIDAY

75 HERONGATE L.M.   English Traditional Melody

I T is a thing most wonderful,
  Almost too wonderful to be,
That God's own Son should come from heaven,
And die to save a child like me.

Bishop William Walsham How (1823–97)

76 HORSLEY C.M.   WILLIAM HORSLEY, 1774-1858

    THERE is a green hill far away
      Without[1] a city wall,
    Where the dear Lord was crucified
    Who died to save us all.

2. O, dearly, dearly has he loved,
    And we must love him too,
    And trust in his redeeming blood
    And try his works to do.
       Mrs. Cecil Frances Alexander (1818-95)

    [1] Outside *may be substituted for* without

EASTER

77 CHRIST OUR LORD IS RISEN Irregular   American Traditional Melody

C HRIST our Lord is risen, Christ our Lord is risen.
Christ our Lord is risen, and lives for evermore,
And lives for evermore, and lives for evermore;
Christ our Lord is risen and lives for evermore.

Norman and Margaret Mealy

78 HAPPY EASTER 8787.8887   JAMES HEATH

COME, ye children, sing to Jesus
On this happy Easter Day,
'Christ, our Saviour, now is risen',
Let his little children say.
All the bells are gladly ringing,
All the flowers are gaily springing,
All the birds with joy are singing;
Come, ye children, praise and pray.

Frederick Smith (1800–73)

79 GAMBLE 6565.D

Adapted from a Melody in JOHN GAMBLE'S
Ayres and Dialogues, 1659

COMING from the winter
Into happy spring,
To our risen Saviour
Easter songs we bring:
Happy, happy spring-time,
Happy Easter Day;
Jesus Christ is risen,
And he lives for aye.

2 Gentle little flowers,
Strong to cleave the sod,
Tell of Jesus rising,
Gentle Son of God:

3 Trees that bud and blossom
At the warm spring's breath
Tell us life is greater—
Greater far—than death:

4. To our hearts this message
Easter Day should give:
They who trust in Jesus
Shall not die, but live:

Walter Hawkins (1857–1949)

80

To be sung to HARVEST SONG, *No.* 74

IT is the joyful Easter-time,
  Let all sing Alleluya!
The merry bells ring out their chime,
They sing their Alleluya.
The Church is bright with flowers gay,
And all Christ's people praise and pray,
For Jesus rose on Easter Day;
Sing joyful Alleluya!

Alda M. Milner-Barry

81 EASTER MORNING 6866   GUTHRIE FOOTE

MORNING in the garden,
  Birds are singing, flowers are springing.
Who walks in the garden?
'Tis Jesus Christ our Lord.

2. We have made a garden,
  Happy garden, Easter garden,
  We have made a garden
  For Jesus Christ our Lord.

Margaret Cropper

THE COMING OF SPRING

82 CROCUS 6565

ELIZABETH HARE

ALL the flowers are waking,
Spring has come again;
God has sent the sunshine,
God has sent the rain.

2 All the trees are waking,
Spring has come again;
God has sent the sunshine,
God has sent the rain.

3 All the birds are singing,
Spring has come again;
Singing in the sunshine,
Singing in the rain.

A verse for Winter

4. All the flowers are sleeping
Underneath the ground;
Sleeping in the winter,
Sleeping safe and sound.

Adapted by Winifred E. Barnard

THE COMING OF SPRING

GUTHRIE FOOTE

I N the lanes and in the parks
Little flowers are showing;
God, who made and loves the flowers
Watches o'er their growing.

2. In the bushes and the trees
Birdsong is beginning;
God, who made and loves the birds,
Listens to their singing.

M. Temple Frere

c 1899

SUMMER TERM

SPRING AND SUMMER

84 THANKFUL PRAISE 7676

Victor Southern

L ET us sing our song of praise;
Thank you, God! Thank you, God!
For the happy Summer days,
Thank you, God! Thank you, God!

2 For the sunshine and the showers,
Thank you, God! Thank you, God!
Bringing us the lovely flowers,
Thank you, God! Thank you, God!

3 For the green and shady trees,
Thank you, God! Thank you, God!
For the gentle cooling breeze,
Thank you, God! Thank you, God!

4. For the birds that sweetly sing,
Thank you, God! Thank you, God!
And for every living thing,
Thank you, God! Thank you, God!

Winifred E. Barnard

85 BOUNTY 6565 and Refrain

WARWICK FARRINGDON

Refrain

SING a song of Maytime,
Sing a song of Spring;
Flowers are in their beauty,
Birds are on the wing.
Maytime, playtime;
God has given the Maytime;
Thank him for his gift of love,
Sing a song of Spring.

2. Blossom on the hedgerows,
   Sunshine on the hills;
   Oh! the happy Maytime
   All my being fills.

Frederick Arthur Jackson (1867–1942)

86 GOD'S WORLD 10 7 9 9.10 8   GEORGE HAYWARD

> THE sun shines down on the beautiful world,
> The world which our Father made,
> And in it the flow'rs and birds and trees
> Are in loveliest colours arrayed.
> God shows us his love in the sunny days,
> We give him our love and our praise.

> 2. The rain comes down on the beautiful world,
> The world which our Father made,
> And in it the flow'rs and birds and trees
> Are in loveliest colours arrayed.
> God shows us his love in the rainy days,
> We give him our love and our praise.

Hilda Margaret Dodd

87 GRATITUDE 767   JAMES HEATH

WE thank thee, heavenly Father,
For all the lovely Spring,
For primroses and bluebells,
And little birds that sing.

2. For woods and fields to play in,
For bright blue sky and sea,
For everything we thank thee;
All beauty comes from thee.

Mary Anderson

88 GOSTERWOOD 7676.D   English Traditional Melody

WE thank thee, O our Father,
　　For all thy loving care;
We thank thee that thou mad'st the world
So very bright and fair.
We thank thee for the sunshine,
And for the pleasant showers;
And we thank thee, O our Father,
We thank thee for the flowers.

C. M. MacSorley

ASCENSION

89

To be sung to EASTER MORNING, *No.* 81

JESUS lives to love us,
   Alleluya! Alleluya!
He is King above us,
Dear Jesus Christ our Lord.

Margaret Cropper

90

To be sung to HARVEST SONG, *No.* 74

THE glad Ascensiontide is here,
   And we sing Alleluya!
To Jesus Christ our Lord most dear
We sing our Alleluya!
A crown of thorns once pierced his brow,
He wears a crown of glory now,
And all the world to him shall bow
With joyful Alleluya.

Alda M. Milner-Barry

SUMMER TERM

WHITSUN

91 CAMBER 6565

MARTIN SHAW, 1875–1958

HOLY Spirit hear us,
   Friend from heaven above
Thou art ever near us,
Fill our hearts with love.

Alda M. Milner-Barry

92   *To be sung to* HARVEST SONG, *No.* 74

IT is the Holy Spirit's day,
   Sing joyful Alleluya!
When all Christ's people met to pray;
Sing joyful Alleluya!
With rushing sound, with heav'nly flame
On them the Holy Spirit came:
They blessed and praised God's glorious name;
Sing joyful Alleluya!

Alda M. Milner-Barry

88

WHITSUN

93 CHRISTUS DER IST MEIN LEBEN 7676

Melody by MELCHIOR VULPIUS,
c. 1560–1616

WHEN God the Holy Spirit
Came down on Whitsunday,
He taught the friends of Jesus
Just what to do and say.

2. When God the Holy Spirit
Speaks to my heart, I know
He'll teach me and he'll help me
And with me always go.

M. E. Knollys

GRACE AT MEALS

94 FOR HEALTH AND STRENGTH 8.6   Melody from *Graded Rounds and Catche*

* *This version must not be used if the tune is sung as a round.*

FOR health and strength and daily food,
We praise thy name, O Lord.

Traditional

ALTERNATIVE VERSION
(as a round)

For health and strength and dai — ly food we

praise thy name, O Lord.

* *One singer begins the Grace and when he reaches (2) the second singer starts to sing from (1). When the first singer reaches (3) a third singer may begin at (1).*

95 DIX (bars 9–12 only) 77   CONRAD KOCHER, 1786–1872

GOD is great and God is good,
And we thank him for our food.

Traditional

90

GRACE AT MEALS

96 TALLIS' ORDINAL C.M.   THOMAS TALLIS, c. 1510–85

T O God who gives us daily bread
  A thankful song we'll raise,
And pray that he who sends our food
Will fill our hearts with praise.

Mary Rumsey (c. 1840)

EVENING

97 TALLIS' CANON L.M.

THOMAS TALLIS, c. 1510–85

GLORY to thee, my God, this night
For all the blessings of the light;
Keep me, O keep me, King of kings,
Beneath thy own almighty wings.

Bishop Thomas Ken (1637–1711)

98 SHIPSTON 8787   English Traditional Melody

JESUS, tender Shepherd, hear me,
  Bless thy little lamb tonight;
Through the darkness be thou near me,
Watch my sleep till morning light.

Mary Lundie Duncan (1814–40)

FOR A BIRTHDAY

99 BIRTHDAY 12 12.8 10   MARTIN SHAW, 1875–195

WE wish you many happy returns of the day!
We hope you may be healthy and strong all the way:
Strong to do right, slow to do wrong,
And thoughtful for others all the day long.

Percy Dearmer (1867–1936)

NATIONAL

Thesaurus Musicus, c. 1743

GOD save our gracious Queen,
Long live our noble Queen,
God save the Queen!
Send her victorious,
Happy and glorious,
Long to reign over us;
God save the Queen!

Anonymous. 17th or 18th century

SUBJECT INDEX OF HYMNS

Subject	*Section*
ADVENT	
Christmas is coming, 58	AUTUMN TERM Advent
ANIMALS	
All things bright and beautiful, 1	GENERAL The World which our Father made
All things which live below the sky, 2	The World which our Father made
God of the rabbits, 5	The World which our Father made
O Father, the maker of beautiful things, 9	The World which our Father made
ASCENSIONTIDE	
Jesus lives to love us, 89	SUMMER TERM Ascensiontide
The glad Ascensiontide is here, 90	Ascensiontide
BEING SORRY	
For the things that I've done wrong, 53	GENERAL Giving and Asking Forgiveness
BIBLE	
God has given us a book full of stories, 20	GENERAL God's Presence, his Blessing and his Care
BIRDS	
All things bright and beautiful, 1	GENERAL The World which our Father made
All things which live below the sky, 2	The World which our Father made
God of the rabbits, 5	The World which our Father made
Thank you! for the world so sweet, 41	Praise and Thanksgiving
All the flowers are waking, 82	EASTER TERM Coming of Spring
In the lanes and in the parks, 83	Coming of Spring
BIRTHDAY	
We wish you many happy returns of the day, 99	BIRTHDAY
BRINGING OF GIFTS. See *Giving*	

Subject	*Section*
FEAR. See *Trust in God*	
FISHERMEN. See *People who work for us*	
FLOWERS	
All things bright and beautiful, 1	GENERAL The World which our Father made
All the flowers are waking, 82	EASTER TERM Coming of Spring
In the lanes and in the parks, 83	Coming of Spring
Let us sing our song of praise, 84	SUMMER TERM Spring and Summer
Sing a song of Maytime, 85	Spring and Summer
The sun shines down on the beautiful world, 86	Spring and Summer
We thank thee, Heavenly Father, 87	Spring and Summer
We thank thee, O our Father, 88	Spring and Summer
FOOD	
Thank you! for the world so sweet, 41	GENERAL Praise and Thanksgiving
We have so much to thank you for, 43	GENERAL Praise and Thanksgiving
When the corn is planted, 57	AUTUMN TERM Harvest
For health and strength and daily food, 94	GRACE AT MEALS
God is great and God is good, 95	GRACE AT MEALS
To God who gives us daily bread, 96	GRACE AT MEALS
FRIENDS	
To God who makes all lovely things, 13	GENERAL The World which our Father made
Let us thank the Heavenly Father, 35	Praise and Thanksgiving
We have so much to thank you for, 43	Praise and Thanksgiving
God has given us work to do, 44	Working for God
GIVING	
Here we come with gladness, 51	GENERAL Giving and Asking Forgiveness
We pray thee, Father, to accept, 52	Giving and Asking Forgiveness
GLADNESS	
I'm very glad of God, 24	GENERAL God's Presence, his Blessing and his Care
Sing a glad song, 38	Praise and Thanksgiving
Sing praises, sing praises, 39	Praise and Thanksgiving
GOD, *The Blessing of*	
Over the earth is a mat of green, 10	GENERAL The World which our Father made

Subject	*Section*
GOD, *The Blessing of (cont.)*	
Be near me, Lord Jesus, 16	GENERAL God's Presence, his Blessing and his Care
Father, see thy children here, 18	God's Presence, his Blessing and his Care
God, the Father, bless us, 21	God's Presence, his Blessing and his Care
GOD, *The care of*	
Gladly lift we hearts and voices, 19	GENERAL God's Presence, his Blessing and his Care
How strong and sweet my Father's care, 22	God's Presence, his Blessing and his Care
I love the Lord who is my strength, 23	God's Presence, his Blessing and his Care
I'm very glad of God, 24	God's Presence, his Blessing and his Care
Into thy loving care, 25	God's Presence, his Blessing and his Care
Loving Father of all children, 27	God's Presence, his Blessing and his Care
Loving Shepherd of thy sheep, 28	God's Presence, his Blessing and his Care
GOD, *The Creator*	
All things bright and beautiful, 1	GENERAL The World which our Father made
All things which live below the sky, 2	The World which our Father made
For the beauty of the earth, 4	The World which our Father made
God of the rabbits, 5	The World which our Father made
God who put the stars in space, 6	The World which our Father made
I love the sun, 7	The World which our Father made
I often think of God, 8	The World which our Father made
O Father, the maker of beautiful things, 9	The World which our Father made
To God who makes all lovely things, 13	The World which our Father made
Hands to work and feet to run, 45	Working for God
The sun shines down on the beautiful world, 86	SUMMER TERM Spring and Summer
GOD, *The Love of*	
I often think of God, 8	GENERAL The World which our Father made

SUBJECT INDEX OF HYMNS

Subject	*Section*
Over the earth is a mat of green, 10	GENERAL The World which our Father made
We praise thee for the sun, 14	The World which our Father made
I'm very glad of God, 24	GENERAL God's Presence, his Blessing and his Care
The King of love my Shepherd is, 29	God's Presence, his Blessing and his Care
All good gifts around us, 30	Praise and Thanksgiving
Now thank we all our God, 36	Praise and Thanksgiving
We have so much to thank you for, 43	Praise and Thanksgiving
The glory of our King was seen, 73	EASTER TERM Palm Sunday
It is a thing most wonderful, 75	Good Friday
There is a green hill, 76	Good Friday
The sun shines down on the beautiful world, 86	SUMMER TERM Spring and Summer
Jesus lives to love us, 89	Ascension

GOOD FRIDAY

It is a thing most wonderful, 75	EASTER TERM Good Friday
There is a green hill, 76	Good Friday

HANDS

Hands to work and feet to run, 45	GENERAL Working for God
Help our lips to praise thee, 46	Working for God
Here are my hands, 47	Working for God
Jesus' hands were kind hands, 70	EASTER TERM Ministry of Jesus

HARVEST

All things bright and beautiful, 1	GENERAL The World which our Father made
Praise and thanksgiving, 37	The World which our Father made
Thank you! for the world so sweet, 41	The World which our Father made
Come, ye thankful people, come, 54	AUTUMN TERM Harvest
See the farmer sow the seed, 55	Harvest
We plough the fields, 56	Harvest
When the corn is planted, 57	Harvest
For health and strength and daily food, 94	GRACE AT MEALS
God is great and God is good, 95	GRACE AT MEALS
To God who gives us daily bread, 96	GRACE AT MEALS

HEALING

We praise thee for the sun, 14	GENERAL The World which our Father made
For all the strength we have, 31	Praise and Thanksgiving
In Galilee beside the sea, 69	EASTER TERM Ministry of Jesus
Jesus' hands were kind hands, 70	Ministry of Jesus

SUBJECT INDEX OF HYMNS

Subject	*Section*

HEALTH AND STRENGTH

We praise thee for the sun, 14 — GENERAL The World which our Father made

For all the strength we have, 31 — Praise and Thanksgiving
Sing a glad song to Christ the King, 38 — Praise and Thanksgiving
Hands to work and feet to run, 45 — Working for God
For health and strength and daily food, 94 — GRACE AT MEALS

HELPING OTHERS

God has given us work to do, 44 — GENERAL Working for God
Hands to work and feet to run, 45 — Working for God
I have a clear message from Jesus, my King, 48 — Working for God
The Holy Child went to and fro, 68 — EASTER TERM Childhood of Jesus
Jesus' hands were kind hands, 70 — Ministry of Jesus

HOLY SPIRIT

Holy Spirit, hear us, 91 — SUMMER TERM Whitsun
It is the Holy Spirit's day, 92 — Whitsun
When God, the Holy Spirit, came down, 93 — Whitsun

HOME AND FAMILY

Let us thank the Heavenly Father, 35 — GENERAL Praise and Thanksgiving
Thank you for my mother dear, 40 — Praise and Thanksgiving
We have so much to thank you for, 43 — Praise and Thanksgiving
I have a clear message from Jesus, my King, 48 — GENERAL Working for God
The Holy Child went to and fro, 68 — EASTER TERM Childhood of Jesus

JESUS, *Childhood of*

Jesus, child of Mary, 67 — EASTER TERM Childhood of Jesus
The Holy Child went to and fro, 68 — Childhood of Jesus

JESUS, *Cross of*. See *Good Friday*

JESUS, *Ministry of*

In Galilee beside the sea, 69 — EASTER TERM Ministry of Jesus
Jesus' hands were kind hands, 70 — Ministry of Jesus

JESUS, *The children's Friend*

Be near me, Lord Jesus, 16 — GENERAL God's Presence, his Blessing and his Care

Jesus, friend of little children, 26 — God's Presence, his Blessing and his Care

SUBJECT INDEX OF HYMNS

Subject	*Section*
Jesus, hear our prayer, 50	GENERAL Working for God
Jesus, child of Mary, 67	EASTER TERM Childhood of Jesus
In Galilee beside the sea, 69	Ministry of Jesus
Riding, riding, 72	Palm Sunday

JESUS, *The Good Shepherd*

Loving Shepherd of thy sheep, 28	GENERAL God's Presence, his Blessing and his Care
The King of love my Shepherd is, 29	God's Presence, his Blessing and his Care
Jesus, tender Shepherd, hear me, 98	EVENING

JESUS, *The King*

Sing a glad song to Christ the King, 38	GENERAL Praise and Thanksgiving
I have a clear message from Jesus, my King, 48	Working for God
All glory, laud, and honour, 71	EASTER TERM Palm Sunday
The glory of our King was seen, 73	Palm Sunday
Jesus lives to love us, 89	SUMMER TERM Ascension

LOVE. See *God, love of*, and *Home and Family*

MOTHER

Let us thank the Heavenly Father, 35	GENERAL Praise and Thanksgiving
Now thank we all our God, 36	Praise and Thanksgiving
Thank you for my mother dear, 40	Praise and Thanksgiving

NATURE. See *God, the Creator*
    Animals
    Birds
    Flowers
    Spring
    Summer
    Winter

PALM SUNDAY

All glory, laud, and honour, 71	EASTER TERM Palm Sunday
Riding, riding, 72	Palm Sunday
The glory of our King was seen, 73	Palm Sunday
To Jesus Christ the children sang, 74	Palm Sunday

PEOPLE WHO WORK FOR US

Down deep dark mines, 3	GENERAL The World which our Father made
When lamps are lighted in the town, 15	The World which our Father made
See the farmer sow the seed, 55	AUTUMN TERM Harvest

Subject   *Section*

PLAY

For all the strength we have, 31	GENERAL Praise and Thanksgiving
Let us thank the Heavenly Father, 35	Praise and Thanksgiving
Sing a glad song to Christ the King, 38	Praise and Thanksgiving

PRAISE

For the beauty of the earth, 4	GENERAL The World which our Father made
To God who makes all lovely things, 13	GENERAL The World which our Father made
We praise thee for the sun, 14	The World which our Father made
Holy God, to thee our voices, 32	Praise and Thanksgiving
Holy, Holy, Holy, 33	Praise and Thanksgiving
I can praise God all day long, 34	Praise and Thanksgiving
Praise and thanksgiving, 37	Praise and Thanksgiving
Sing a glad song to Christ the King, 38	Praise and Thanksgiving
Sing praises, sing praises, 39	Praise and Thanksgiving
Help our lips to praise thee, 46	Working for God
To Jesus Christ the children sang, 74	EASTER TERM Palm Sunday

QUEEN

God save our gracious Queen, 100	NATIONAL

RAIN. See *Sunshine and Rain*

SEEDTIME. See *Harvest*

SPRING

Coming from the winter, 79	EASTER TERM Easter
All the flowers are waking, 82	Coming of Spring
In the lanes and in the parks, 83	Coming of Spring
Sing a song of Maytime, 85	SUMMER TERM Spring and Summer
We thank thee, Heavenly Father, 87	Spring and Summer

SUMMER

Let us sing our song of praise, 84	SUMMER TERM Spring and Summer
Sing a song of Maytime, 85	Spring and Summer
The sun shines down on the beautiful world, 86	Spring and Summer
We thank thee, Heavenly Father, 87	Spring and Summer
We thank thee, O our Father, 88	Spring and Summer

SUN, MOON, AND STARS

For the beauty of the earth, 4	GENERAL The World which our Father made

SUBJECT INDEX OF HYMNS

Subject	*Section*
God who put the stars in space, 6	GENERAL The World which our Father made
I love the sun, 7	The World which our Father made

SUNSHINE AND RAIN

We praise thee for the sun, 14	GENERAL The World which our Father made
Let us sing our songs of praise, 84	SUMMER TERM Spring and Summer
The sun shines down on the beautiful world, 86	Spring and Summer
We thank thee, O our Father, 88	Spring and Summer

THANKSGIVING

All good gifts around us, 30	GENERAL Praise and Thanksgiving
For all the strength we have, 31	Praise and Thanksgiving
Let us thank the Heavenly Father, 35	Praise and Thanksgiving
Now thank we all our God, 36	Praise and Thanksgiving
Praise and thanksgiving, 37	Praise and Thanksgiving
Thank you! for the world so sweet, 41	Praise and Thanksgiving
Thank you, God, for all you give us, 42	Praise and Thanksgiving
We have so much to thank you for, 43	Praise and Thanksgiving

TRUST IN GOD

Father, lead me day by day, 17	GENERAL God's Presence, his Blessing and his Care
Gladly lift we hearts and voices, 19	God's Presence, his Blessing and his Care
How strong and sweet my Father's care, 22	God's Presence, his Blessing and his Care
I love the Lord who is my strength, 23	God's Presence, his Blessing and his Care
I'm very glad of God, 24	God's Presence, his Blessing and his Care

WINTER

God of the rabbits, 5	GENERAL The World which our Father made
All the flowers are waking (*Winter verse*), 82	EASTER TERM Coming of Spring

WISE MEN. See *Epiphany*

WHITSUN. See *Holy Spirit*

WORK

Father, see thy children here, 18	GENERAL God's Presence, his Blessing and his Care

SUBJECT INDEX OF HYMNS

Subject		*Section*

WORK (*cont.*)

God has given us work to do, 44	GENERAL	Working for God
Hands to work and feet to run, 45		Working for God
Here are my hands, 47		Working for God
Jesus bids us shine, 49		Working for God
Jesus' hands were kind hands, 70	EASTER TERM	Ministry of Jesus
The Holy Child went to and fro, 68		Childhood of Jesus

ALPHABETICAL INDEX OF TUNES

ALPHABETICAL INDEX OF FIRST
LINES OF HYMNS

ALPHABETICAL INDEX OF FIRST LINES

PRINTED IN GREAT BRITAIN
AT THE UNIVERSITY PRESS, OXFORD
BY VIVIAN RIDLER
PRINTER TO THE UNIVERSITY